SOUL HITS

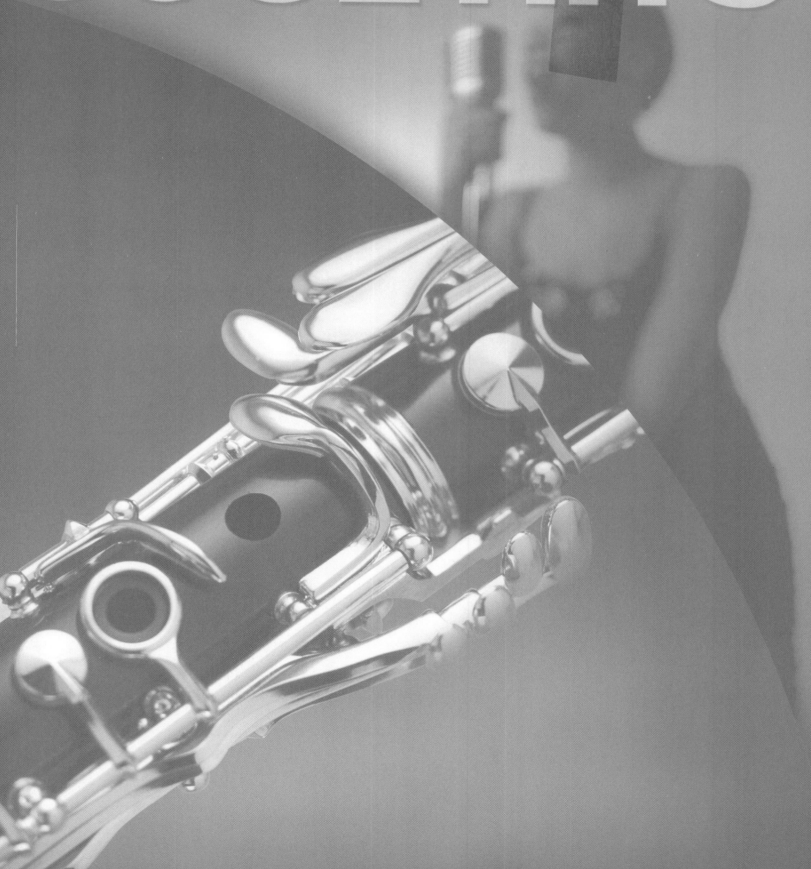

Clarinet

INSTRUMENTAL PLAY-ALONG

SOUL HITS

SOLO ARRANGEMENTS OF 15 GREAT SOUL SONGS WITH CD ACCOMPANIMENT

HOW TO USE THE CD ACCOMPANIMENT:
A melody cue appears on the right channel only.
If your CD player has a balance adjustment, you can adjust
the volume of the melody by turning down the right channel.

This publication is not authorised for sale in
the United States of America and/or Canada

HAL LEONARD EUROPE
DISTRIBUTED BY MUSIC SALES

Exclusive Distributors:
Music Sales Limited
14-15 Berners Street, London W1T 3LJ, UK.

Order No. HLE90003474
ISBN: 978-1-84772-521-9
This book © Copyright 2008 Hal Leonard Europe

Printed in the USA

Your Guarantee of Quality
As publishers, we strive to produce every book to the highest
commercial standards. The book has been carefully designed to
minimise awkward page turns and to make playing from it a real
pleasure. Throughout, the printing and binding have been planned
to ensure a sturdy, attractive publication which should give years
of enjoyment. If your copy fails to meet our high standards,
please inform us and we will gladly replace it.

www.musicsales.com

Contents

◆ GREEN ONIONS

Clarinet

Written by AL JACKSON, JR., LEWIS STEINBERG,
BOOKER T. JONES and STEVE CROPPER

2 I GET THE SWEETEST FEELING

Clarinet

Words and Music by
VAN McCOY and ALICIA EVELYN

❸ I GOT YOU (I FEEL GOOD)

Clarinet

Words and Music by
JAMES BROWN

◆ I SAY A LITTLE PRAYER

Clarinet

Lyric by HAL DAVID
Music by BURT BACHARACH

❖ IN THE MIDNIGHT HOUR

Clarinet

Words and Music by
STEVE CROPPER and WILSON PICKETT

◆ LET'S STAY TOGETHER

Clarinet

Words and Music by AL GREEN,
WILLIE MITCHELL, and AL JACKSON, JR.

Moderately

7 PICK UP THE PIECES

Clarinet

Words and Music by JAMES HAMISH STUART,
ALAN GORRIE, ROGER BALL, ROBBIE McINTOSH,
OWEN McINTYRE and MALCOLM DUNCAN

◆9 RESPECT

CLARINET

Words and Music by
OTIS REDDING

◆8 PRIVATE NUMBER

Clarinet

Words and Music by
BOOKER T. JONES and WILLIAM BELL

Medium Rock

10 (SITTIN' ON) THE DOCK OF THE BAY

Clarinet

Words and Music by
STEVE CROPPER and OTIS REDDING

◆ SOUL MAN

Clarinet

Words and Music by
ISAAC HAYES and DAVID PORTER

🔷14 WALKIN' THE DOG

Clarinet

Words and Music by
RUFUS THOMAS

◆12 STAND BY ME

Clarinet

Words and Music by BEN E. KING,
JERRY LEIBER and MIKE STOLLER

🔷13 TAKE ME TO THE RIVER

CLARINET

Words and Music by
AL GREEN and MABON HODGES

🔶15 WHO'S MAKING LOVE?

CLARINET

Words and Music by
BETTYE CRUTCHER, DON DAVIS,
HOMER BANKS and RAYMOND JACKSON